Welcome to *Grow in Love*

Dear Families,

Welcome to Grow in love for Senior Infants/P2. As you know by now, schools today are happy places, where children learn lots about themselves, about each other, and about the world around them. As you have chosen to send your child to a Catholic school, some time each day is also spent helping your child to learn more about God.

Grow in Love is a programme designed to be used both in school and at home. It will also provide links with the local parish community. Each week, your child will ask you to help them to do something related to the programme at home. We encourage you to take this opportunity to teach your child about the faith which you chose for them in Baptism, and continue to pass on to them every day. With the support of the teachers in your school and of your parish community, we hope that it can help you to journey with your child as they 'grow in love' with God and with one another.

IN SCHOOL

David knew that God was with him

Colour and write.

AT HOME

God is with me

Read this poem with your family.

This week, we help the children to see that God is always with them, loving them and caring for them. God's love comes to them through their families and people who care for them.

God is with me

If I hide under a ,
God is with me

If I swim in the deep blue ,
God is with me

If I am stung by an angry ,
God is with me

If I fall and scrape my ,
God is with me

If I have (pasta) for my tea,
God is with me

At any time at all, you see,
God is with me.

Chat Together
About how God is always with us, watching over us and loving us.

Pray Together
Help your child to make the *Sign of the Cross*, and to pray the words: In the name of the Father, and of the Son, and of the Holy Spirit. Amen.

IN SCHOOL

God created ...

Finish the pictures and colour.

AT HOME

God also created people

Chat together about all the things people can do. Your family can help you write something under each picture.

This week, the children hear the story of creation from the first book of the Bible.

What can you see?

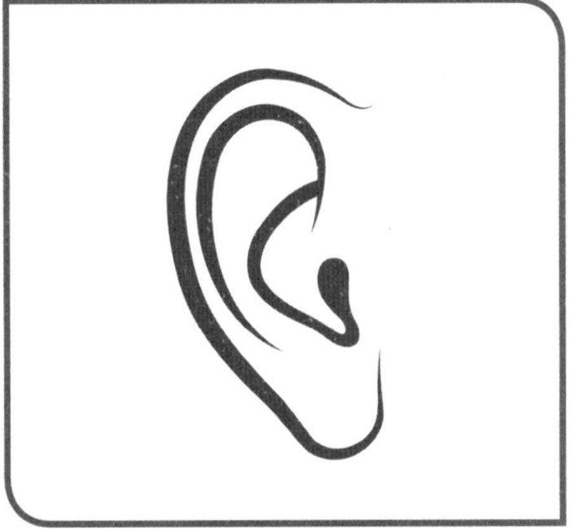

What can you hear?

What can you smell?

Pray Together

For the wasp and the bee, say 'Glory be!'
For the plant and the tree, say 'Glory be!'
For the lakes and the sea, say 'Glory be!'
For you and me, say 'Glory be!'

What can you taste?

What can you touch?

IN SCHOOL

What is your favourite part of creation?

Draw and colour.

AT HOME

David loved creation

Read the story with your family.

This week, we tell the children about how King David loved all of creation.

Once there was a boy called David. His job was to mind sheep. David loved being outside, and he loved looking at all the things that God had created: the sun, the moon, the stars, the birds and the trees.

David thanked God for the water his sheep drank and the grass they ate. He said 'How wonderful God is!'

As he got older, David wrote many psalms to give thanks and praise to God for all the wonderful things in the world.

Chat Together
About your child's favourite part of God's creation, which they drew on p. 6. Tell your child about your favourite part of creation.

Pray Together
Glory be to the Father,
And to the Son,
And to the Holy Spirit.
As it was in the beginning,
Is now, and ever shall be,
World without end. Amen.

IN SCHOOL

We can care for the world

Circle and colour the people who are caring for the world.

AT HOME

Caring for the world

Chat together about the ways in which your family can care for the world using the pictures below:

This week, we talk to the children about how they can care for the world that God made.

Pray Together

Morning Prayer, asking God to help us to show love for one another, and for the world, every day.

Father in heaven, you love me,
You're with me night and day.
I want to love you always
In all I do and say.
I'll try to please you, Father.
Bless me through the day.
Amen.

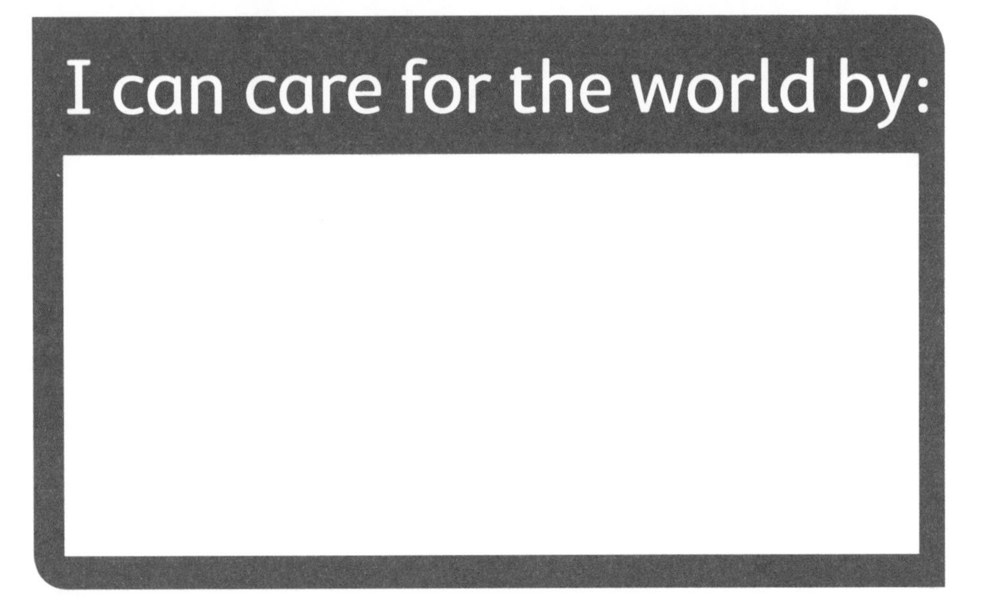

IN SCHOOL

What things does your family like to do?

Colour the things you do together.

AT HOME

This is our family

Draw your family or paste a photo into the box. Write the names of the people in your family.

This week, we help the children to understand that they belong in your family. We talk about the things your family like to do together, and the ways in which you can show love to each other.

Chat Together
About all the things you love about your children, for example, the way he/she gives hugs, makes you laugh, share his/her toys, etc.

Pray Together
Loving God,
Bless our home and our family.
Help us to continue to show love for each other.
Amen.

IN SCHOOL

Our family lives here

Draw a picture of some of the things you can see in the community where your family lives.

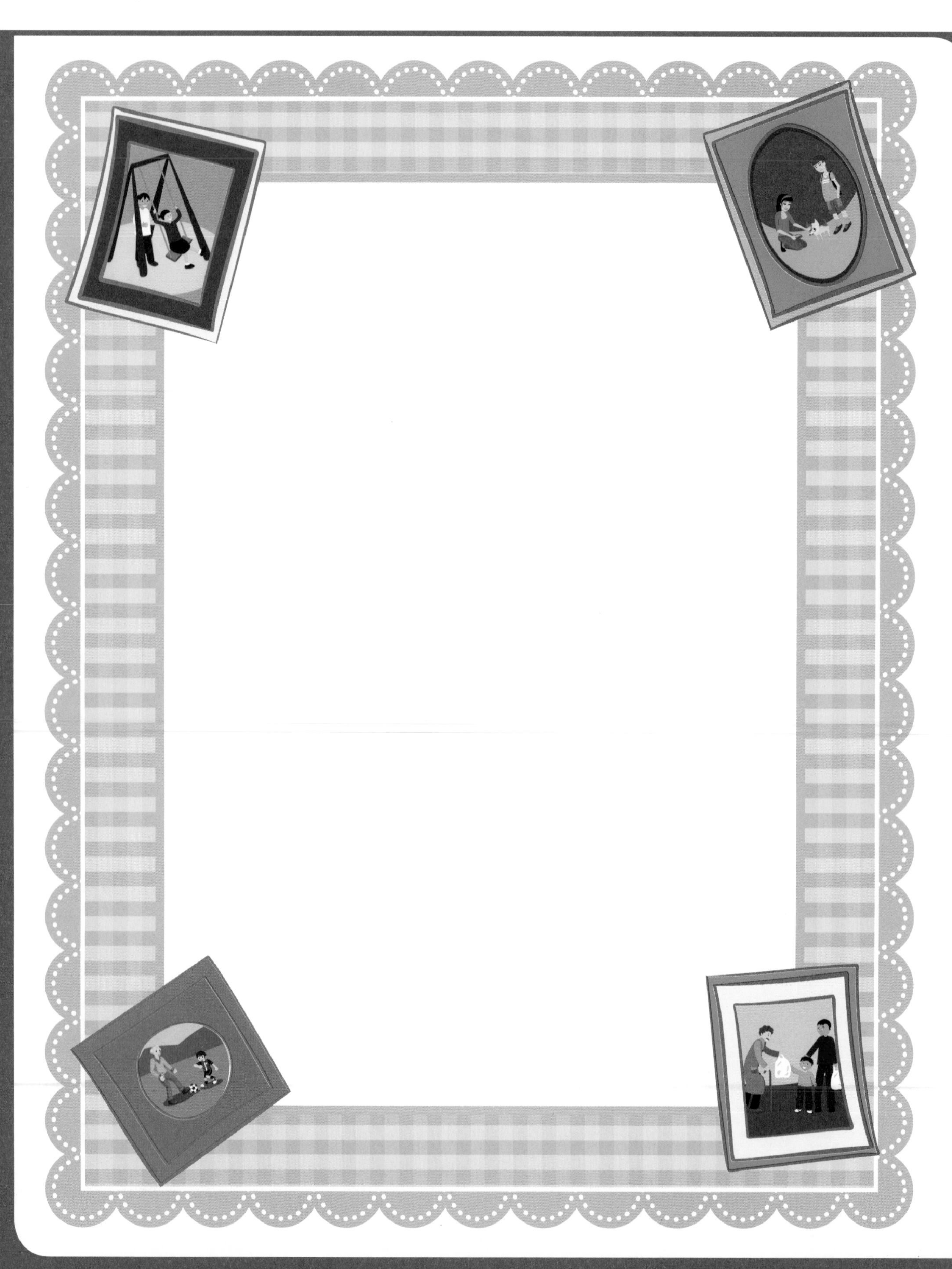

AT HOME

We care for our community

Chat together about the different ways that you and your family can care for the community in which you live. For example:

This week, we chat with the children about the community to which your family belongs. We help them to see the ways in which they can be part of that community.

Pray Together
Loving God,
Bless all those who are part of our community.
Help us to share our gifts to make our community a great place to live.
Amen.

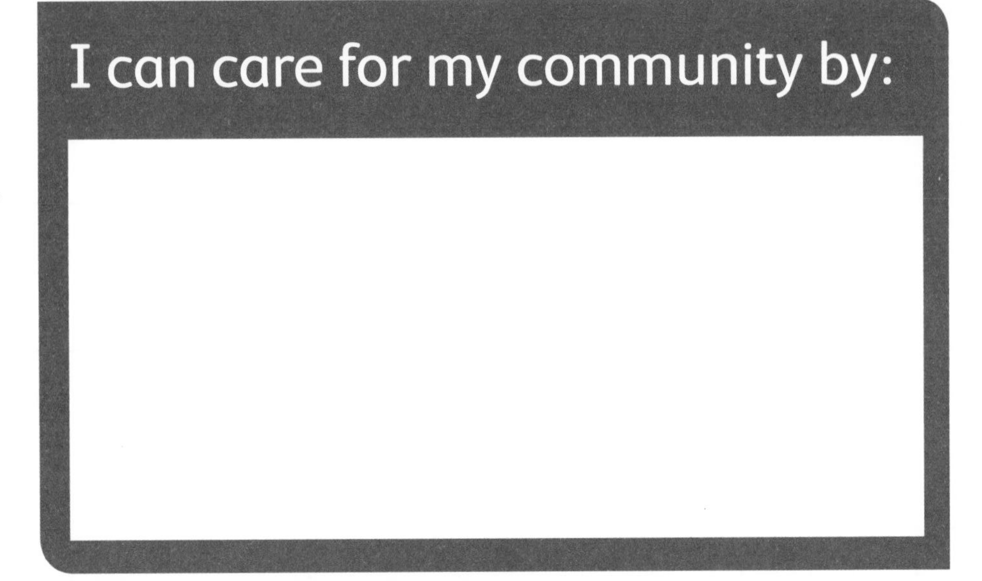

IN SCHOOL

One family

All the people in the world are part of one human family. God loves everyone. Draw your family and friends in the picture.

AT HOME

Mother Teresa

Read the story of Mother Teresa with your family.

This week, we teach the children that all people in the world are part of the one human family. We tell them the story of Mother Teresa, who showed love to people who were poor and those who were sick.

There once lived a woman called 'Mother Teresa'.

Teresa lived in a city called Calcutta. Many people who were poor lived there.

Teresa spent a lot of time talking to God and listening to God.

She knew God wanted her to help other people.

So, Teresa went to live with the poorest people she could find in the city of Calcutta.

She also cared for people who were sick. Soon, other women came to help her.

Chat Together

About the different ways in which you and your child can be kind to others, especially those who are in need.

Pray Together

Loving God,
Help us to learn from the lives of Mother Teresa, and other holy men and women.
Help us to show love to all people.
Amen.

IN SCHOOL

Jesus teaches his friends to pray

Write the words. Draw Jesus' friends and colour the picture.

AT HOME

Our Father

Say this prayer with your family.

This week, we introduce the children to the Our Father*, the prayer that Jesus taught to his friends, and the prayer that the friends of Jesus still say today.*

Our Father, who art in heaven,
hallowed be thy name;
thy kingdom come,
thy will be done
on earth as it is in heaven.
Give us this day our daily bread,
and forgive us our trespasses,
as we forgive those who trespass
against us;
and lead us not into temptation,
but deliver us from evil.
Amen.

Chat Together
Jesus taught his friends to say this prayer. As Jesus' friends, we can say this prayer too. How else can we show that we are Jesus' friends?

Pray Together
Our Father (see prayer in box opposite).

IN SCHOOL

What things do we need in winter?

Circle and colour the things we need in winter.

AT HOME

The Advent wreath

Colour three candles purple and one candle pink. Draw a flame over one purple Advent candle this week.

This week, we teach the children that Jesus is the Light of the World. Our celebration of his birth on Christmas Day will light up the winter days. Advent is the time we spend getting ready to celebrate Jesus' birth.

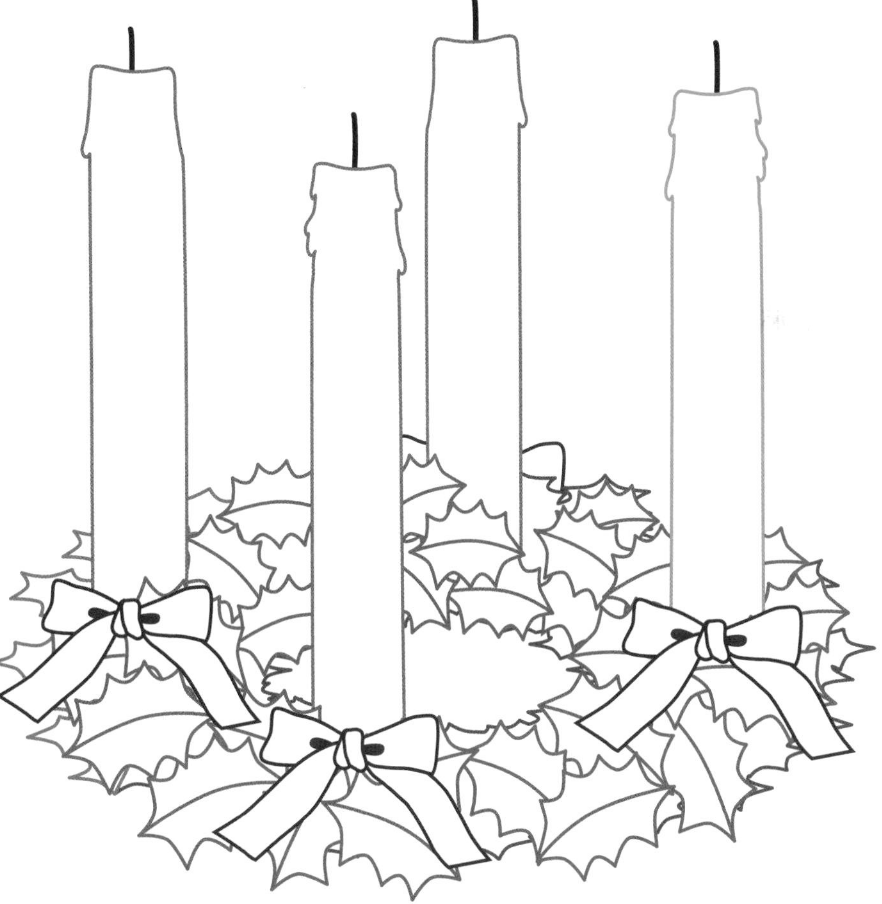

Chat Together

About the signs of winter that you and your family can see: colder weather, darker days, leafless trees etc. What are you looking forward to about Christmas? Bring your child to the church this week to see the Advent wreath.

Pray Together

Loving God,
Bless all of us this wintertime.
Keep us warm, safe and happy.
Bless people who do not have warm houses to sleep in, or hot food to eat.
Amen.

IN SCHOOL

The Angel Gabriel comes to Mary

Help the angel Gabriel find the way to Mary.

AT HOME

Hail Mary

Write the words and colour the picture.

This week, we tell the children about Mary. God chose her out of all the women in the world to be the mother of his Son, Jesus.

Hail Mary, full of grace,
The Lord is with thee.
Blessed art thou among women,
and blessed is the fruit of thy womb, Jesus.
Holy Mary, mother of God,
pray for us sinners now,
and at the hour of our death. Amen.

Chat Together
About the different ways that you can honour Mary in your home. Maybe you could pray the *Hail Mary* together, or help your child to draw a picture of Mary that you could put in your home. The next time you are in the church, show your child the statue of Mary there.

Pray Together
Draw a flame over a second purple Advent candle on p. 19. Pray the *Hail Mary* together (*See prayer in box opposite*).

IN SCHOOL

Who was in the stable?

Join the dots. Draw the picture.

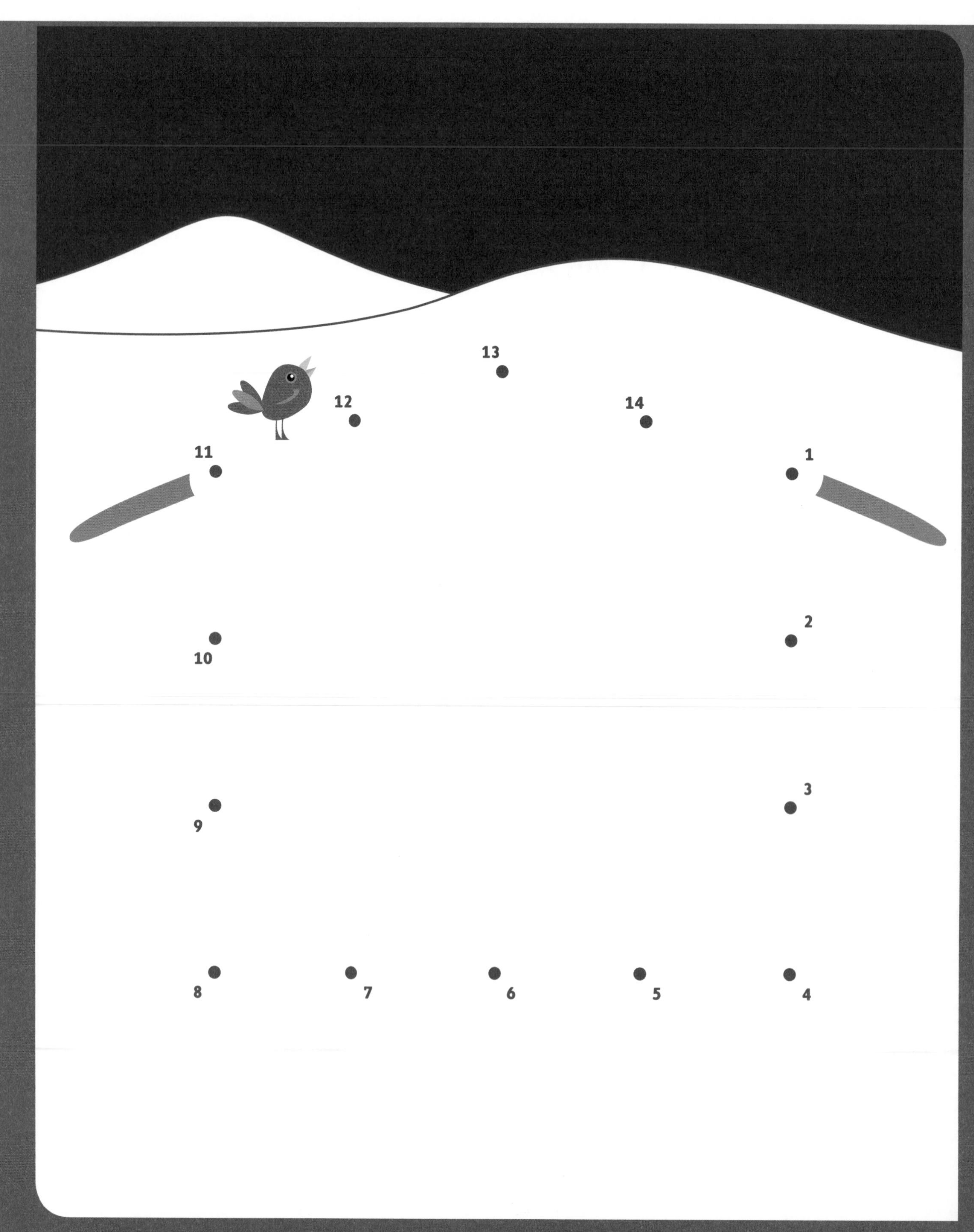

AT HOME

The Present

Read this poem with your family.

This week, we teach the children that Jesus was God's gift to the world. God sent Jesus into the world to show us how much he loves us. Jesus taught us about God. Jesus was God's gift of love.

The poor little boy was as sad as could be.
He had no present for under the tree.
'Oh, my Mammy and Daddy work so hard for me,
I have nothing to give them to thank them you see.'

But, later, alone, on his small little bed,
he took bright coloured paper and long bits of thread.
And he tied up a parcel with nothing inside,
and he crept down the stairs when the parcel was tied.
When he woke the next day, he went down to the tree,
he saw Mammy and Daddy as glad as could be.

'We got perfume, a tie and a clock for the shelf,
but your present is special, you made it yourself.
And your bright little parcel, all tied up and small,
was filled up with love,
the best present of all.'

Chat Together
About the things that your child gives you that you cannot wrap and put under the tree. Tell your child, 'I love your hugs', 'I love the way you make me laugh', etc.

Pray Together
Draw a flame over the pink Advent candle on p. 19 and say this prayer together:

Loving God,
Thank you for our homes and our families.
Bless those who don't have anyone to give them gifts this Christmas.
Amen.

IN SCHOOL

Who told the shepherds that Jesus had been born?

Draw and colour.

AT HOME

Who visited the stable?

Circle and colour.

This week, we tell the children that the shepherds and the wise men visited the stable in Bethlehem. There they found Jesus, Mary and Joseph.

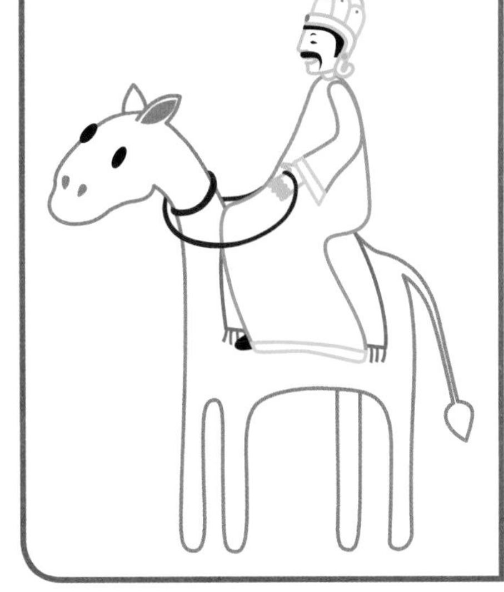

Chat Together
About the gifts that the wise men brought to Jesus – gold, frankincense and myrrh. Chat about what gifts your child would have given the baby Jesus.

Pray Together
Draw a flame over the last purple Advent candle on p. 19. Then sing a Christmas carol such as *Away in a Manger* or *Mary, Will you Take this Baby Boy?* with your child.

IN SCHOOL

Simeon and Anna meet Jesus

True or False? Colour the ☺ or the ☹.

Mary and Joseph took Jesus to the temple.

There, they met an old man called Tom.

They also met a woman called Anna.

Jesus, Mary and Joseph lived in Dublin.

AT HOME

Jesus is God's greatest gift

Write the words.

This week, we tell the children the story of how Mary and Joseph brought Jesus to the temple soon after he was born. There they met an old man named Simeon and a woman called Anna. When they saw Jesus, they knew that he had been sent by God.

Chat Together
About what made Jesus such a special child. In what ways was he the same as every other baby? What was different about him?

Pray Together
For all newborn babies that you know, or any families who are waiting for a baby to be born. Ask God to bless those families and their babies.

IN SCHOOL

The Holy Family lived in Nazareth

Where do you live? Write and draw.

Jesus, Mary and Joseph lived in Nazareth

We live in:

AT HOME

Jesus lived in Nazareth

Read this poem with your family.

This week, the children learn about how Jesus, Mary and Joseph, who are known as the Holy Family, lived together in Nazareth.

Jesus lived in Nazareth
in a little house of stone.
With Mary and with Joseph too,
it was a happy home.

Mary cared for Jesus well
and taught him how to pray.
They loved spending time together
in their happy home each day.

Chat Together
About the things that the Holy Family did together: eating, praying, telling stories, playing, visiting relations, etc. In what ways is your family like the Holy Family?

Pray Together
Prayer to our Guardian Angel, which your child has been learning at school*:*

Angel sent by God to guide me,
Be my light and walk beside me;
Be my guardian and protect me;
On the paths of life direct me.
Amen.

IN SCHOOL

St Brigid was ...

Mark the words that describe St Brigid. Colour the picture.

kind

mean

loving

caring

selfish

AT HOME

Tell the story ...

Read the story 'St Brigid and the apples' with your family.

This week, the children learn the story of St Brigid. Brigid was a kind person. She was especially kind to people who were poor. She wanted to show them that she loved them, and that God loved them too.

One day, Brigid set out on a long journey.

She stopped to rest at the side of the road.

A woman stopped and gave her some apples.

Some people who were poor came by.

Brigid shared the apples with them.

They knew that Brigid was a special person.

Chat Together
About the ways in which your child can be kind, like St Brigid.

Pray Together
St Brigid of Ireland
Help us, we pray,
To be kind and loving
In our work and play.

Spring has sprung!

Colour the trees as they look in spring, summer, autumn and winter.

AT HOME

Thank you, God, for spring

Circle the signs of spring. Colour the picture.

This week, we help the children to watch out for the early signs of spring. These signs remind us that God is continuing to take care of the world and everything in it.

Chat Together
About the signs of spring that your family can see. What are you looking forward to most about the arrival of the spring?

Pray Together
Before bed this evening, pray together, thanking God for all the things that he has given to us by saying the *Night Prayer*:

God, our Father, I come to say
Thank you for your love today.
Thank you for my family,
And all the friends you give to me.
Guard me in the dark of night,
And in the morning send your light. Amen.

IN SCHOOL

We hear stories from the Bible

Can you recall the Bible stories you have heard? Draw your favourite.

AT HOME

'I remember ...'

Ask your parents to tell you a story about something that happened when you were younger. Draw a picture to go with the story, or paste a photo of the event in the box below.

This week, we help the children to realise the importance of telling stories. We get to know people when we hear their stories. We learn about ourselves when we hear stories of our family's past. Soon, we will hear more stories about Jesus. These stories will help us to get to know Jesus better.

Pray Together

Make the *Sign of the Cross*, and name all the people in the story you told your child. Ask God to bless them. Finish your prayer by saying any prayer on the inside back cover of this book.

IN SCHOOL

What did the boy have in the basket?

Draw the food in the basket and colour the picture.

AT HOME

Jesus feeds the people

Help the boy find his way to Jesus.

This week, we teach the children a new story about Jesus. This story tells how he fed a large crowd of people with just five loaves of bread and two fish. We call this a miracle story.

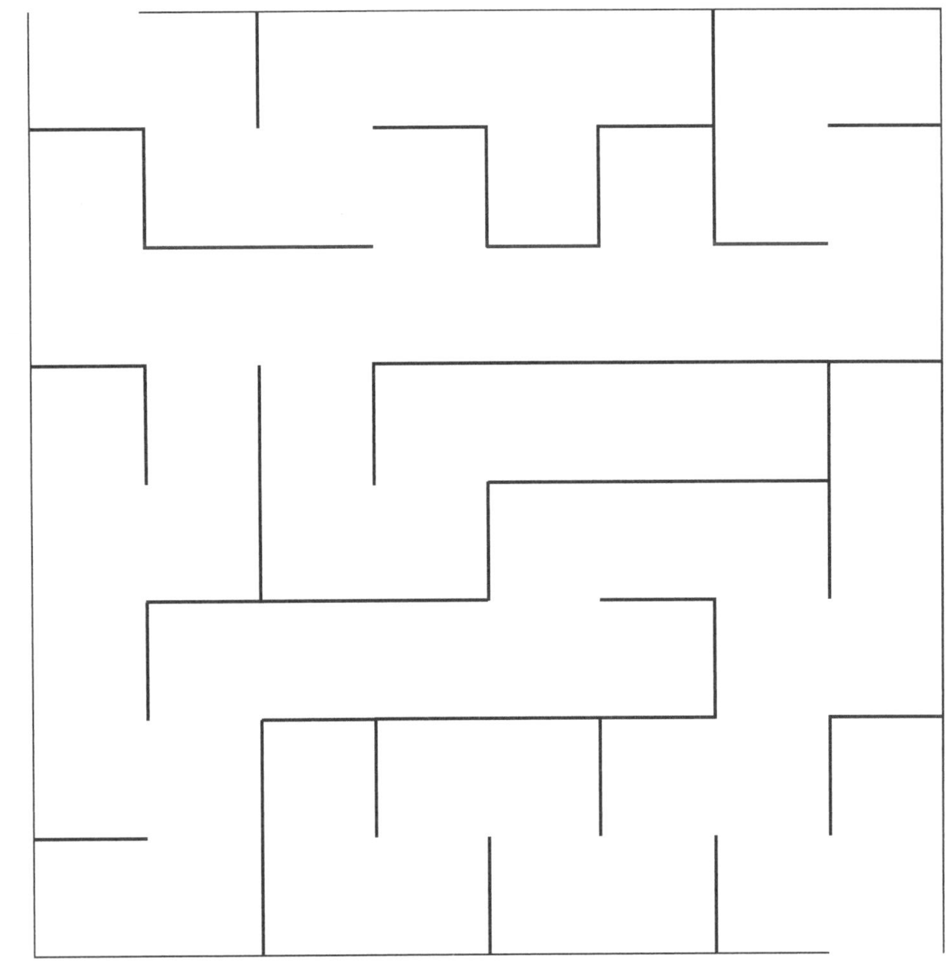

Chat Together
About the generosity of the little boy in giving Jesus what little food he had. Chat with your child about times that he/she has shared with others.

Pray Together
Before and after your evening meal today, pray the *Grace before Meals* and the *Grace after Meals* together:

Grace before Meals:
Bless us, O God, as we sit together.
Bless the food we eat today.
Bless the hands that made the food.
Bless us, O God. Amen.

Grace after Meals:
Thank you, God, for the food we have eaten.
Thank you, God, for all our friends.
Thank you, God, for everything.
Thank you, God. Amen.

IN SCHOOL

Jesus calms the storm

What did Jesus say to the storm? Write and colour.

AT HOME

How were Jesus' friends feeling during the storm?

Colour the correct faces.

This week, we teach the children a second new story about Jesus. This story tells about how he calmed a storm on the Sea of Galilee.

Chat Together
About times when your child is afraid. When Jesus' friends were afraid, they asked him to help. Chat about who your child can talk to when he/she needs help.

Pray Together
Jesus, our friend,
We know that you are always listening to us.
Thank you for being there when we need you.
Help us to listen to others, and to help them when we can.
Amen.

IN SCHOOL

Our eyes are important

Circle and colour your favourite things to look at.

I like to look at:

AT HOME

Jesus helps a man to see

Read the story 'Jesus helps a man to see' with your family.

This week, we tell the children a third new story about Jesus. This story tells how he healed a man who was blind.

Jesus and his friends were walking along the road.

A man who was blind was sitting at the side of the road.

The man shouted, 'Jesus! Help me!'

Jesus called the man over.

Chat Together
About why Jesus helped the man who was blind. When have you/your child felt the need to help someone?

Pray Together
Loving God,
Thank you for the gift of sight.
Help us not to take it for granted.
Bless those who cannot see.
Amen.

Jesus healed the man.

The man became one of Jesus' friends.

IN SCHOOL

What things did Jesus and his friends need for the Last Supper?

Colour and circle.

AT HOME

The Last Supper

Draw Jesus and his friends at The Last Supper.

This week, we tell the children the story of Jesus' last meal with his friends, which we now call The Last Supper.

Chat Together
Jesus said to his friends, 'Do this in memory of me'. In what way does your family remember Jesus? Do you pray together, go to Mass together or talk about Jesus?

Pray Together
Jesus, our friend,
Help us to remember you
when we visit the church,
when we say a prayer
when we talk about you,
And when we hear stories about you.
Amen.

IN SCHOOL

Jesus dies on the cross

Draw a picture of Jesus on the cross.

AT HOME

Jesus dies on the cross

Help Mary and Jesus' friends find their way to the place where Jesus died.

This week, we remind the children of how Jesus died. Jesus was put to death on a cross because some people didn't like what he was saying or what he was doing. They didn't want to live like him. They didn't want to love others or to be kind to others.

Chat Together
About how some people wear a cross or crucifix, or have one in their homes, to show that they are Jesus' friends. Where can your child see a cross or crucifix?

Pray Together
Jesus our friend,
You taught us that God always loves us,
And you taught us to show love to one another.
You showed love to everyone you met.
Help us to show that we remember you by doing the same.
Amen.

IN SCHOOL

Jesus' death was not the end!

Number the pictures 1–4 to put them in the correct order, then colour them.

AT HOME

How did his friends feel when they saw the Risen Jesus?

Colour the correct faces.

This week, we teach the children the story of how the Risen Jesus appeared to his friends on the shores of the Sea of Galilee after his Resurrection.

Chat Together
About how your family might celebrate Easter this year: by going to Mass on Holy Saturday night or Easter Sunday, by visiting the church, etc.

Pray Together
Jesus is risen!
Alleluia! Alleluia!

IN SCHOOL

King Solomon's house of prayer

Finish and colour the house of prayer.

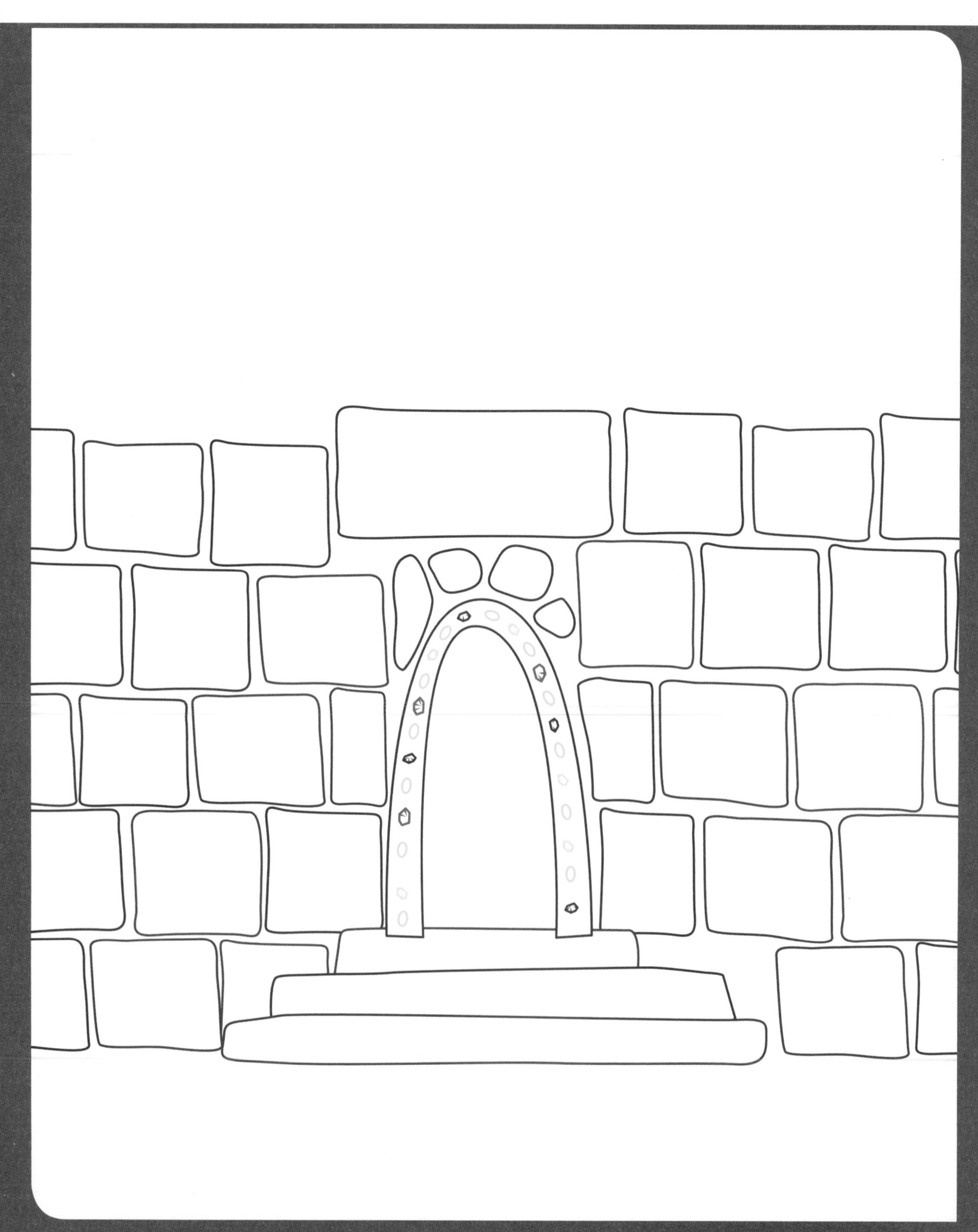

AT HOME

Our parish

Fill in the blanks with your family.

This week, we tell the children the story of how King Solomon built a house of prayer, where all the people in his kingdom could go to pray to God.

We live in ________________ parish.

The priest(s) in our parish is/are:

____

______________________________________.

This is a picture of the church in our parish:

Chat Together
About your local church: what is its name? What do you like about it? What family occasions have you celebrated there? Make a plan to visit the church together.

Pray Together
Loving God,
Thank you for our church.
Bless the people who
go there to pray.
Bless the priests and people
who work in the church.
And bless us, today and every day.
Amen.

IN SCHOOL

What do you see in the church?

Match the words and the pictures.

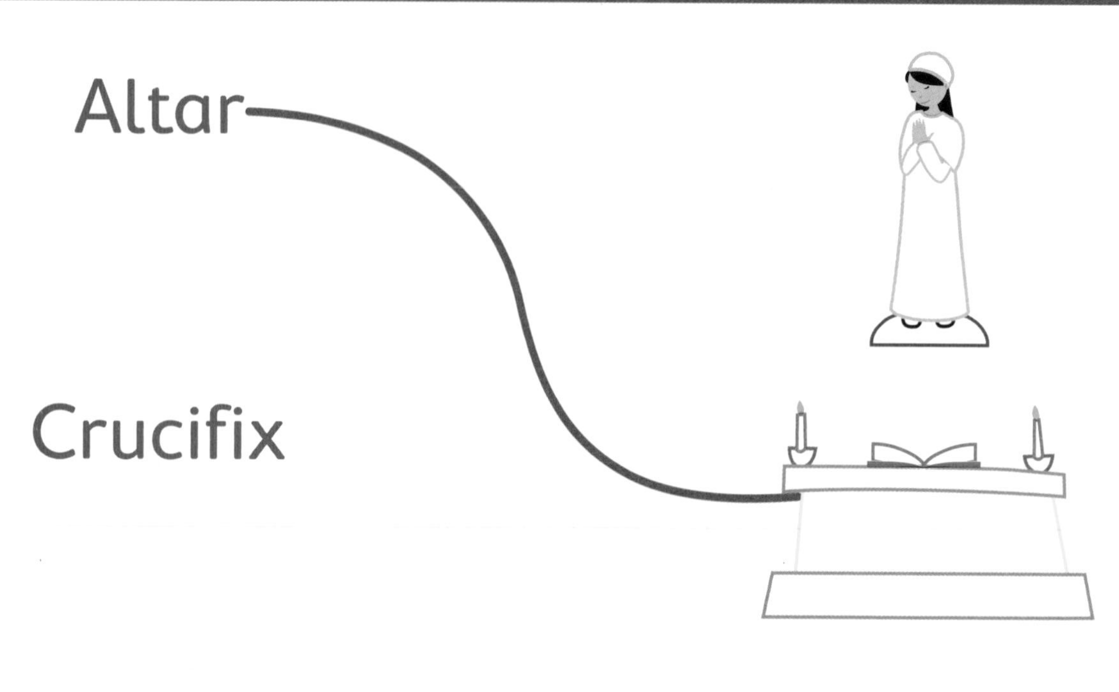

Altar

Crucifix

Baptismal Font

Paschal Candle

Statue

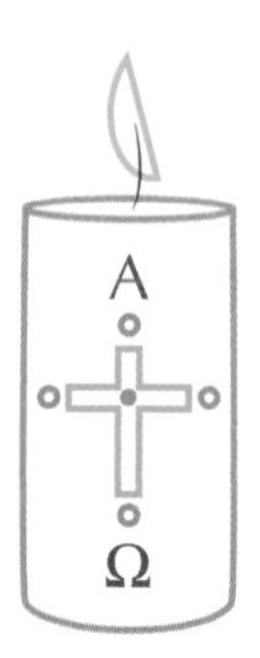

AT HOME

Our church

Go on a visit to your local church. Draw some of the objects in the church. Ask your family to help.

This week, we teach the children about the objects in the church building. We also chat about some of the ways we can show respect in the church: by being quiet, by kneeling and by genuflecting.

Chat Together
About how your child can show respect in the church. Teach your child to genuflect by showing him/her how to bend his/her right knee to the ground.

Pray Together
Each week, at Mass, we pray the prayer that Jesus taught us, the *Our Father*. Say that prayer together this week. You will find it on the inside back cover of this book.

IN SCHOOL

Elizabeth's Baptism

Circle and colour the things Elizabeth's family needs for her Baptism.

AT HOME

My Baptism

Fill in the blanks with your family. Draw a picture or paste on a photo of your baptism.

This week, we chat to the children about a baby's Baptism. We introduce the candle, white garment and holy water as the symbols used in Baptism.

The priest who baptised me was Fr ________________ (name).

I was baptised in ____________________ Church.

The name my family chose for me was ______________________.

Chat Together
About your child's Baptism: Who was there, what he/she wore, the priest who was there, how you celebrated the occasion, etc.

Pray Together
Make the *Sign of the Cross* on your child's forehead, as you did on the day he/she was baptised.

IN SCHOOL

John baptises the people

Draw the people who wanted to be baptised by John. Colour the picture.

AT HOME

What did John tell the people to do?

Read together and colour the pictures.

This week, we teach the children about John the Baptist. John told the people to be good and kind and honest. He also told them to be baptised to show their love for God.

Be kind

Share

Pray

Say 'sorry'

Chat Together
About how your child can be kind, share, pray and say 'sorry' when they have done something wrong. When they do these things, they show their love for God.

Pray Together
Loving God,
Help us to show that we are your friends,
By being good, kind and honest.
Help us to say sorry when we do something wrong.
Help us to share what we have with others.
Amen.

IN SCHOOL

Which children made good choices?

Colour and circle.

AT HOME

I can make good choices

How well do you do each of these things? Colour the ☺, 😐 or ☹.

This week, we talk to the children about how they can make good choices. When we make good choices, we live as Jesus taught us.

Listening.

Helping at home.

Sharing.

Saying 'please' and 'thank you'.

Forgiving.

Chat Together
About times when your child made good choices. Share with your child times when you made good choices, and how you felt about it.

Pray Together
Jesus, our friend,
Help us to live as you taught us to.
Help us to make good choices now and always.
Amen

IN SCHOOL

In November, we pray for those who have died

Talk about the things you can do to remember and colour the pictures.

Eternal rest grant unto them,
o Lord.
May they rest in peace.

AT HOME

We remember ...

Draw a picture or paste a photo of someone who has died.

This week, we help the children to remember someone they know who has died.

We remember:

____

______________________________.

Chat Together
About the person who has died. We believe that God wants those who have died to live with him in heaven.

Pray Together
Eternal rest grant unto
____________, O Lord.
May he/she rest in peace. Amen.

IN SCHOOL

Lent is a time to say sorry

Circle the pictures of the people who need to say sorry. Colour the pictures.

AT HOME

I can say that I am sorry'

Mark the four words you would use to tell God that you are sorry.

This week, we talk to the children about Lent. This year, they learn that Lent is a time to say sorry for the things that we have done wrong.

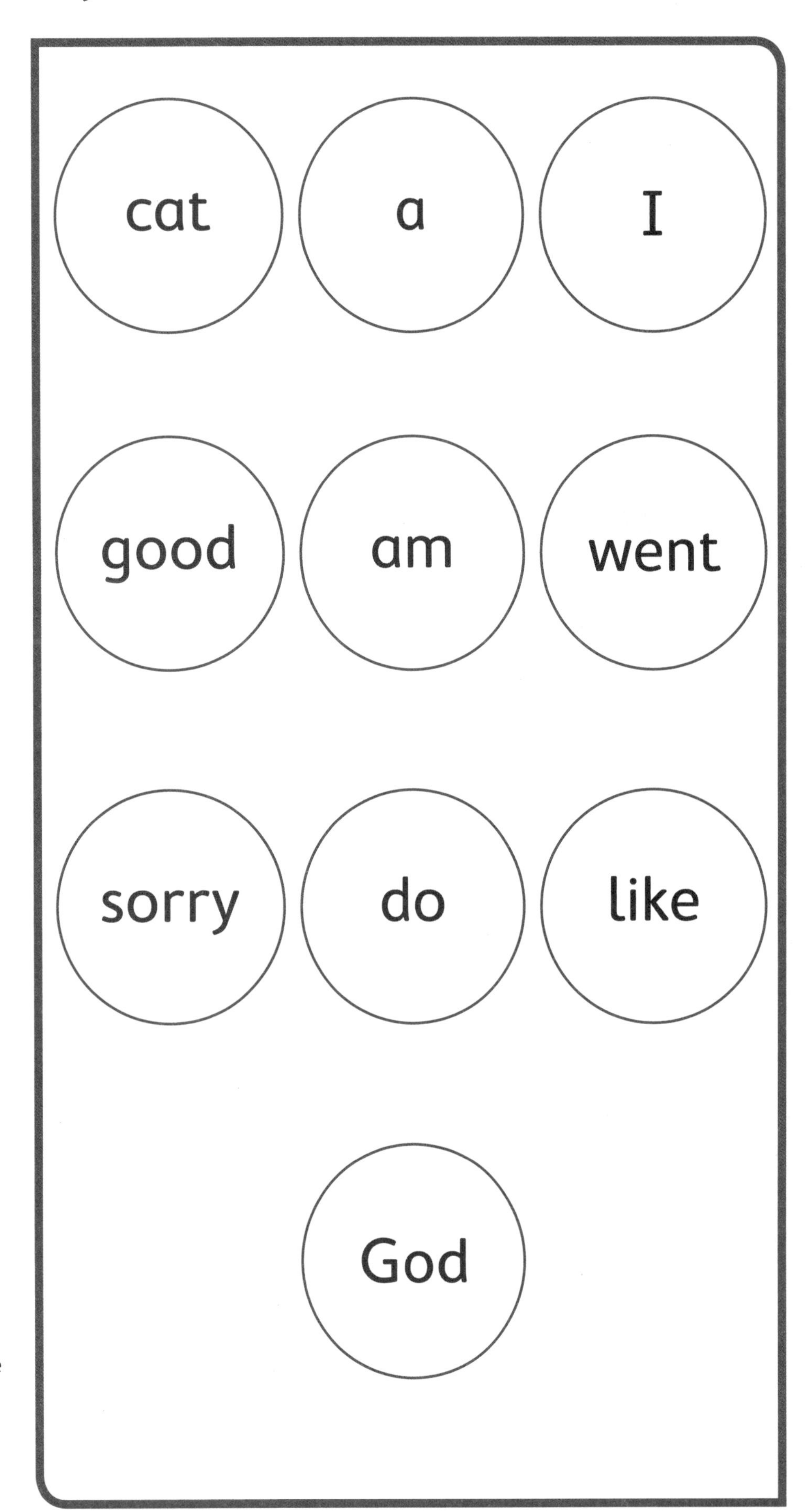

Chat Together
About a time when your child said sorry. Then tell your child about a time when you were sorry for something you did that was wrong. Tell your child how you tried to make up for what you had done.

Pray Together
God our Father,
Thank you for always loving me.
Sometimes, I do not love others the way I should.
Help me to be sorry, and to try again.
Amen.

IN SCHOOL

What would you put on the May altar?

Draw and colour.

AT HOME

May is the month of Mary

Read the sentences about Mary with your family.

This week, we help the children to think about the ways that they can honour Mary, the Mother of Jesus, during the month of May.

An angel came to to tell her that she would be the mother of Jesus.

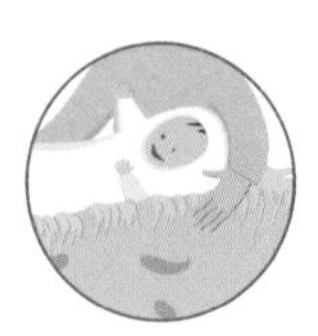 was born in Bethlehem.

When grew up, he taught people all about God.

During May, we can honour in a special way.

Chat Together
About the ways that your family can honour Mary during May, for example by displaying a statue or picture of Mary in your home this month, or by visiting a church to see a statue of Mary.

Pray Together
Hail Mary, which you will find on the inside back cover of this book.